CANCER
BOWS TO A
Smile

Volume 1

Bruce Morton

Cancer Bows to a Smile
Volume 1

Bruce Morton

Acknowledgements

This is where I'm supposed to thank everyone I've ever met for making me the person I am today. That is to include Mr. Miller my 8th grade biology teacher who taught me how to cut up a frog. Truth be told, that guy always gave me the creeps and smelled of a combination of Brylcreem and Sen Sen.

This book and its digital offspring would not exist were it not for the dedication and hard work of my friend Gryf Ketcherside. Gryf took my postings from Facebook and formed them into this book. That, my friends, was a LOT of work.

Thank you, Gryf.

Contents

Foreword

You have before you a series of postings and comments made to Facebook private groups that have grown up to serve those of us who have the blood cancer Multiple Myeloma.

The postings start out rather ordinary but as they continue two things start to happen. First, my journey with the disease becomes more challenging... I get sicker. And second, to better cope I decided to do a bit of mood modification by writing only uplifting postings, my mission being to stay in a positive frame of mind no matter where this cancer took me. So I posted light hearted recounts of my day with the MM.

Others in the private group found my postings funny. A relief from the daily grind of this illness.

Cancer Comedy. Tumor Humor. Strange, Huh? But all of us sorely needed to laugh more. And as we did smile and laugh more , if even for just a short while , we felt just that little bit better.

So the others encouraged me to write more. The positive comments included here may look like my attempt to glorify myself so let's be clear. It's never been about me. It's been a collective effort to bring a smile and a laugh to our lives as we travel with this cancer.

You will also learn about what it is like to travel with MM. So many challenges to health, relationships, attitude and one's faith life.

The postings have not been edited for typos. Spell checker software makes for some interesting word replacements that are left in. For privacy reasons I have removed the names of those who commented. I truly believe that a smile and a laugh is good medicine. Yes, Cancer Bows to a Smile.

bruccemorton@sbcglobal.net

On January 2

January 2, 2019

Ok. I'm throwing in the towel on my New Years' Resolution to be more persistent. Don't criticize me for giving up as I went twice as long as last year.

Sleep

January 7, 2019

Sleep. What are our sleep patterns? Lately my sleep has been mostly in short bursts but last night, whew! A goner in the recliner… somehow, sometime, made it to the bedroom and the dog had to nose me up but not until 9:00am ... Do you occasionally sleep for as long as 12 hours? Hello! Wake up! Hey, yeah you! Wake up and write a response. Come on .. up and at 'em...

Comments:

Oh yes! I have '12 hour sleep sessions.' Get home at 5. Bed by 7pm. Awake the next morning with alarm at 6:30 am.

BGM After a long sleep like that I'm well rested and set for adventure today. Yes. Today's the day. Shoestrings! Shoes that have real shoestrings. None of that Velcro today. I'm going to bend over and tie real shoestrings. Ok. Here goes...

I sleep a ridiculous amount. Since about two years ago.

Well Monday-Friday...up- at 6:00... I LIVE for Saturdays when I don't have to get up until I'm darn good and ready! Sometimes that might be 9:00 AM sometimes it might be 2:00 pm! Actually all of my friends know not to call or text before 10:00 on Saturdays unless it's an emergency! LOL

So...is it the waking in the night that most troubles me, or could it be the foodfest that has been following?? A week on Prednisone and my entire internal register has gone out of whack. Yes, I admit to sleeping on the recliner during the daylight hours, but this wakey every couple of hours is driving me to... eat.

I could sleep all day and night since my SCT four weeks ago! I can be talking with a friend who's come to visit and the next thing I'm asleep! It's rather annoying, I hope it dissipates soon!

Prayer Request

January 11, 2019

A bit of a prayer request here. My center posted my immunoglobulin numbers from today's labs just now and we have quite a significant jump in my important Lambda Light Chain marker. I'll call my MM specialist concerning this on Monday.

Ah ha. A bit of drama ahead for me soon, methinks…

As expected I am indeed coming out of the deep response I've enjoyed since May 2018. We will now wait until I am symptomatic of the MM and formulate a new treatment scheme , most likely a clinical trial. But perhaps not. All is good . This is no surprise. My markers have been ticking up since last Fall.

Comments:

I'm sending you all the positive energy I can muster! Hang in there, Bruce.

I hope your doctor comes up with a good plan so you don't have to suffer.

Stay calm, try not to worry (easier said than done, I know) sending good wishes.

Don't stress just yet—my lambda numbers have been hovering around 120 to 140 for more than 2 years now, but still no treatment.

Oh hate to hear that Bruce ! Good vibes & prayers friend.

Sending healing thoughts

this too shall pass

Start of Year 7

January 20, 2019

Just realizing it's January 20. January 17, 2013 was my date of MM diagnosis. We are 3 days into our 7th year of the journey. Praise God.

Someday This Will Be Funny

January 23, 2019

"Someday this will be funny too." We've all heard that hooey. But sometimes it can be true.

My fall in the kitchen on Monday. Funny? You decide.

Falls often start out with one small mistake that balloons into calamity. Initially my mistake was to leave the dishwasher door down. Oh and I was wearing my favorite loose fitting Crocs. Oh and I've recently started taking Gabapentin for neuropathy in my feet. (A Google search reveals a side effect of Gaba is being "unsteady"... Who knew?)

See where this is going?

So, he bangs his shin against the open dishwasher door which further adds to his "unsteady" state.

Next his feet come completely out of his loose Crocs and to further add to his "unsteady" his feet are now atangle with the loose Crocs on the floor.

Here is the official start of the "fall"... When asked "Any falls." by the doc he must fess up.

Down like a sack of sand but not without a feeble attempt to save himself by grabbing at a pan and a skillet.

His head careens off the shelf where sits the coffee maker .

Pan spins at his feet... skillet in his lap.

The dog is ga ga gone sensing soon the first responders will be arriving. She likes first responders.

And just as quickly as it began it was over. The fall is now category "had" not "having".

He assesses possible damage done and Praise God, he is ok.

He is reminded. It's not about the fall ... it's about the sudden stop!

Take care, fellow MM travelers.

"Someday this will be funny, too"

Cryotherapy

January 29, 2019

Cryotherapy for peripheral neuropathy. Google it. With early morning temperatures predicted to be -5 here, I'm thinking that taking a stroll around the neighborhood in flip flops and my Speedos may be just the ticket for my aching feet. What say ye, group? Is this a good idea? (Hey! Get past the visual picture you have in your head right now of me in Speedos. That's not the point. This may be a breakthrough in cost saving therapy for neuropathy!)

I Thought He Had Cancer…

February 8, 2019

Ok. Today in the journey it's off to the cancer center to see my MM specialist and get my labs for this month. My important number is trending up... it more than doubled last month.... so we may have to intervene and that will be... count 'em... the start of my fifth line of therapy. Yikes!

I've been at this a while. I'm into my 7th year since dx, so I've probably waited for lab results well over 60 times now. Double yikes!

I've learned that I can't much influence the direction of that important marker number , however I can absolutely and directly influence the peace I experience each day of my MM journey.

This day is a gift for me to enjoy fully and I shall.

May your day be filled with peace and confidence also.

So let's start the day with a smile so big they will all wonder "What's up with him? I thought he had cancer!"

Marker Doubled

February 9, 2019

Ok fellow MM travelers, yesterday was my appointment with my MM specialist at the cancer center and as I expected it would, my important marker has doubled since last month... it had doubled the previous month also. So if it doubles next month I'll have scored an MM "hat trick"... a triple double!

We are waiting for me to show more symptoms which historically I have at these marker levels. Then I'll get a PET scan and then we'll search out a magical fifth line of therapy for me.

Enough of all that. Yeah, the MM is progressing and this 10 month long chemo break will soon end. And Mr. Dex will likely once again be my travel companion. And yadda yadda ...

Yesterday at the center though, was all good. I got a close parking spot....She found a vein on the first stab...The wait for the doc was a long one (Ugh!) so I slipped over to the infusion lounge where they all know me from previous IV days. (There's one nurse there that I just KNOW is hot for me.) I snatched TWO bags of Cheetos Ha!...

Told the doc a joke better suited for a five year old, but we all laughed just the same.

And then I was outta there and made it home by my nap time.

What a wonderful gift of a day!

Valentine's Day

February 14, 2019

Ok fellow MM travelers... it's Valentine's Day... my 7th since my dx. Now my first couple Valentine's Days I spent alone and in a funk. No Valentines would arrive and there was that whole thang about my incurable cancer to gnaw on.

Not any more though.

These last few Valentine's Days have been marvelous ... I look forward to this day. Huh? What? You are alone and you have cancer ... marvelous? ... how's that possible?

Well, I make it a point early on each Valentine's Day to conduct my own outreach program to show as many people as I can that cancer has not in the least limited my ability to experience love.

So I call out, text or message folks and tell them "I love YOU."

No fist bump "Love ya, man" or lame "You are loved." Nope. Point blank. In your face. Index finger jabbed to the chest: "I love YOU."

I don't wait around for that call to come to me saying those three words. Ha! Ain't gonna happen.

So I'll call my 94 year old stepfather:

"Cal. This is Bruce. I love YOU!"

And my caregiver sister Karen. My prayer warrior Brett.

And Bright Eyes.

The list goes on and on and this day will be FILLED with love.

Now isn't that what we want on this day? To push aside our cancer and experience love.

So, reach out and make it happen, eh.

Valentine's Day

February 14, 2019

To all you MM travelers on this Valentine's Day. I love you all for getting up each day to take in this cancer as your unwanted companion. It's not easy.

I'm proud of you and I love YOU!

Phase 1 Trial

February 28, 2019

Ok fellow MM travelers I'm starting on the next leg of my journey.

I've signed up for a clinical trial. My first. It's a Phase 1 trial... FIH (First in Human)... that's open to just 90 participants worldwide. I'll be further tested for eligibility next week. BMB. EKG. CMP. CBC. LLC. EE-EYE-EE-EYE-OH.

My MM is progressing which makes me eligible for consideration . This will be my fifth line of therapy.

Truth be told, this therapy may not be the "silver bullet" for me personally... it's so early in development they frankly just don't know how the drug will work against MM. Can you say "hopefully optimistic?"

This trial is to look for response against MM and to establish dosing protocols. Looks like I'll be given 160mg in hospital... at least for the first doses.

We are excited about this opportunity to help launch a new drug to treat MM. This drug is in a class by itself directed at a totally unique target.

Every MM drug being used today started out life in a Phase 1 trial.

Since this trial is FIH the previous recipients were mice. But they've suggested that maybe just maybe it will add years to my life. What they did not explain was whether they meant mouse years or human years. Hmmmmm.

Join The Group

March 3, 2019

Ok, those with MM raise your hand.

Ok now those with a raised hand who travel this MM journey with a wife, a husband, a significant other, etc., drop your hand. This message is not for you. Sorry.

Still have your hand up? Great! Now is the time to consider joining our FB private group Partners: MM Support Group for Those Facing MM Without a Significant Other.

(Abbreviated PMMSGFTFMMWASO)

No really, you should join.

We daily discuss and explore MM issues that are unique to our MM journey without a significant other. We support each other. We encourage each other. We've been known to laugh. And, when there's a need, to cry together.

Use the link below to get signed up by the person responsible for this wonderful group.

Come on in... lurk for as long as you like before you post.

Link here...see you inside...

https://www.facebook.com/groups/245511492825052/

Join The Group

March 3, 2019

Hello to everyone in our FB private group Partners: MM support group for those facing mm without a significant other (Abbreviated PMMSGFTFMMWASO) Pronounced "Pug-mmmm-suh-guh-fi-mmm-wao-ah-so" Rolls off the tongue like butter sauce don't it? Check over on the other two main FB support group postings. We put together a post to recruit others to join this group.

Would you all please post your own personal invitation in a comment to that post? More is better. We want to grow our support for others out there like us.

I Used To ____________

March 5, 2019

Ok fellow MM travelers here's somephin to consider this day of our journey.

Can you think up a particular thang that you used to enjoy doing to the fullest but now because of your MM you've had to limit in this "new normal".

So tell us how you've adapted and risen above that seeming limitation.

Hmmmm . Yeah. Now think on that...

HEY! Keep it clean! This is PG rated group. (Well on most days anyway.)

Now we don't need to dwell on the "can't anymore" side of the equation... let's try to share a "but now I ________ and that's fine" side of things.

It's as simple as filling in the blanks:

I used to enjoy __________ing. But now I __________. And that's fine.

I said KEEP IT CLEAN! Geez some people...

I'll start.

I used to enjoy fishing all day. But now I fish less and sit on the bank more. And that's fine.

I used to enjoy lots of face to face interaction. But now during the flu season it's best for me to limit that. And that's fine.

I used to enjoy getting thru a meal without spilling. But now I just bring the roll of paper towels to the table and that's fine.

I used to know where my feet were... I could FEEL them. But now with the neuropathy I just look down and whoa they're still there. I can SEE them. And that's fine.

So...

Seeming limitations and how you are adapting.

Post yours....

So Thankful

March 7, 2019

An unusual early hour for me to write but I'm wide awake. I spent all day yesterday being tested for eligibility in the Phase 1 trial I've signed up for.

I am just so THANKFUL.

I am thankful to God for allowing me the gift of the day .. we got through it all just fine. I'm so thankful to my sister who is my caregiver.

I am thankful that I got my favorite close parking spot... short walk in 10 degree weather... brrrrr!

First stop was that heart test where they place all those sticky electrodes on your skin and I am SO thankful that chemo took all my body hair! The electrodes pulled right off! Then to the lab and I'm so thankful she was gentle (I don't have a port) and 18 tubes later I was outta there and I got a peppermint!

To the BMB. I am so thankful to nurse Gina. Gentle Gina. This time I was given Demerol and Ativan injection prior to the biopsy which called for additional size sample for the trial. A big glump of my marrow is in route to the drug company. Special thanks to the Demerol .. honestly I didn't feel a THING during BMB. Thankfully It's all behind me now! Ha!

I'm thankful Mr. Demerol accompanied me to full skeletal X-ray and the normally ice cold table felt... felt... come to think of it I wasn't feeling anything. And the nurse had this interesting Eastern European accent as I recall.

On to more tests... it's 2:00 in the afternoon, I veer when I walk but I'm still upright. Though, sadly , I don't remember any of the additional tests as Mr. Demerol is in full command and he is so wonderful.

I'm brought home and deposited into bed... one friend comes over to visit and I'm thankful for friends and their good sense to know when to scram.

It's now 4:00 pm and I am thankful for the wonderful power nap 'til 9:00pm.

I'm so thankful for the leftover pizza that warmed nicely on the dry cast iron skillet. Yum.

Still loopy I decide to check my messages as I knew some folks would want to hear a story or two about my day... so thankful for friends , aren't we, eh. (I was taught "eh" by my one Canadian friend. They say "eh" like all the time , eh.) Messaging. I messed that up. Still loopy. I'm so thankful that after just a few contacts I gave up and me and little Lord Demerol went back to bed until about 4:30am.

Now I'm up.

Thankful for coffee... toast and SEEDLESS boysenberry jam.

Thanks for listening .

Be thankful for all we are allow to experience this day of our journey.

Comments:

So glad to hear all went smoothly for you Bruce!!! Excited about traveling this journey with you my Friend. And I Love Mr. Demerol!!!☺

Great story and I will try to remember that friend and call on him when I get to that stage. 😂😂*. Glad all is well my friend!* 🙌💪.

It's a Journey, Not a Battle

March 9, 2019

Is MM cancer an "invader" to battle? (Ahem... truth be told I'm not much of a badass warrior. In a barroom brawl my best badass would collide soundly with a REAL badass who would play whup ass on my sorry ass. I'm more of a proud tired ass.)

Or, the concept was eloquently stated on another post that MM cancer is an "unwanted guest" we are charged to accept. Hmmm I sorta like that.

I'll respond to those approaches to MM with my own.

Yes to the concept of "unwelcome guest" (vs. an "invader" that we "fight" and "battle.")

I even go so far as to consider my cancer as ME... some of MY cells have gone rogue. I travel WITH MY cancer. It's an acceptance to what IS for now but will change as time goes on. This day with my cancer is a GIFT to enjoy not just a day to battle. No matter how "bad" my cancer is on any particular day I can live with it... accept it... push back on it. But I'm not in a brawl with it...

What say ye?

Comments:

awwwww, you are AWESOME, You are brave and dare I say a f#%^ing W#%^r Nooe, I wont. You do YOU ☺ whatever we do to make it through this crazy journe called life, whatever we need to believe. No one knows but YOU. LOVE, LOVE your attitude. Damn, what a journey you have had.

My cancer is a demon from hell who hides within my body, watching for a weak point and time to re emerge.

Lets fight like warriors that we are

I have cells that are stubborn and smart. Just like me! Sometimes I have to tell at them to listen because they want to do their own thing. Just like me! Right now I want them to work very hard at making healthy new stem cells. For my future me!

I love your attitude. It will really help you on this pilgrimage. Sorry about my rant, I am an optimist and realist. I am a walking prayer, meditator, positive affirmator and feel incredibly blessed to still be her against all odds

Gratitude and Love is what has gotten me through the worst parts, as has acceptance of what is and surrender 🙌.

I don't see mm as a battle as much as I do the opportunity to let God lead me.

I agree! I don't battle. I make the best of what I got. Always have.

My experience with multiple myeloma has taught me some good things about myself and my family that I could not have learned without having gone through cancer. All the things that I have learned during this year, and the things I will learn in the next year while going through chemo and stem cell transplants, will be been important to my growth spiritually and emotionally. I would not trade one day with cancer to a life time without. I am stronger and more resilient than I ever thought I could be while being faced with my own mortality.

I prefer think of MM cells as being confused cells that need to be escorted out of my body by ' magic medicines' ..... Kind of like a loud drunk @ a bar...the MM cells bear me no ill will & are just as confused as to how they got there as I am..

I've never liked the fight mantra...I don't need anymore stress hormones..😉

If you don't like the word cancer, do what I do, call it a hemato-oncological disorder.

I still have had more problems from the treatments than the disease, but I khow what it does without the treatments, so onwards to the SCT!

Good for you 💪👍😮 Healthy attitude ❤. Mine feels like a terrorist that has invaded my body and has a grenade with the trigger off ready to drop at any time. I used to think like you, "a happy life interrupted" as Tom Brokaw said. 6 years later, two stemcells, too many ER visits to count, 14 lines of treatments, all of which have failed, a child with four anxiety disorders because she has had to live with a mom who has aggressive mm since she barely thrned seven and besides me and my husband she has no family, and yes, I see myself as a badass warrior, cause if I wasn't I would have thrown in the towel a long time ago when I was in the hospital and could not even shower or wipe my own butt because a 9 cm tumor showed up in less than two months and made me feel like I had broken my back. We all do what we can, say what we need to say and call it what we need to call it 🙂😮

I take the view it is a part of who I am now. I have found that less stressful than being a warrior and thinking I have to fight it all the time.

God's got this! I trust Him! God bless you!

Another Saturdee Night

March 9, 2019

"Well...

Another Saturdee night and I ain't got nobody..."

Ah Sam Cooke at his best.

Well, noooooooo.

Not so fast buster! You are not alone in your MM journey, you are a part of this "Partners" FB group and this is your invitation to take a role in making our group somephin for everyone. So let's hear from you. Somephin on your mind about your MM or in your personal life now that you have MM? We'll make up a post topic that interests you and let others join in.

No Saturdee night longing . Ya hear! Nope.

No pining away to be spooning with a special someone.

Yes that spooning is wonderful.

Or not. Suppose that special someone got just a bit of stank...or all sweaty...or worse yet STICKY.

Or noisy when they sleep. (One of my exes... I have two so far... used to snort like a race horse. Ooooo. Scare me!)

So hey. Connect wiff others here who are in the same "boat", eh. Bring a smile. A story. Got the "blues", yeah that too. Post a personal concern to others who have a special understanding.

Mmmmmm , yeah

"I got some money cause I just got paid..."

Sing it Sam...

Comments:

Another Saturday nigh ✎..... rock in Bruce ! And thank you for your awesome inspiration!

I like to listen to my favorite songs from my early 20s makes me smile

Was supposed to go to a Hotel California- Eagles Tribute Band concert tonight and bagged it. Lousy day today, migraine headache at 5:30am, took two lots of Relpax to get rid of it and then I cried the whole day for no good reason. Total waste of a day.

Introducing Myself

March 15, 2019

Ok... This site is new. I'll introduce myself.

I'm in St. Louis, Missouri where our economy is multifaceted. One of facet of our economy is... ugh... yeah... well... it's crime. But we're working on that and in the meantime us old folks just do our business in the daylight hours and it works out ok.

I was dx in 2013. I am Lambda Light Chain only, no M spike.

I've burned through 4 lines of therapy and I'm praying to be accepted into a Phase 1 clinical trial for a new drug that, if it works, might someday benefit lots of others with MM.

I'll only post positive... for me, each day that I am allowed to remain is a gift. And I choose to live my life with MM to the fullest. My belief is that cancer bows to a smile. When I post I hope to have you smiling with me.

Help me learn about MM here through you and what you've experienced in your MM journey.

Since I know this site is truly "MM patients only" I'd like to post details of how I'm doing in my clinical trial here.

But first I need to be accepted into the study. I'll update you on that when I know more.

And now... your turn to say something about yourself if you care to share this day of the journey...

FIH Trial

March 15, 2019

I'm new here as everyone else is and I have some exciting news.

I just got the call today that I've been accepted into a new clinical trial to help develop a brand new drug in the treatment of mm.

This is a Phase 1 FIH (First In Human) trial that will be the first attempt to discover if the drug works against MM and at what dosages.

This is exciting. New treatment approaches must be explored. Every single currently approved MM drug started out in a Phase 1 trial.

I go in to the hospital on Sunday and I'll get my first dose perhaps the next day. They want me there for the first doses which is understandable. It's a single agent pill in this trial.

The trial is open to just 90 participants and a few are already taking the drug. So I'm not the first. And my MM is progressing, though quite slowly. So if this doesn't work on my MM there'll be ample time to switch me to some other therapy. So... no worries, eh.

With your permission... if you'd like to hear... I'll update this group on my experiences in a clinical trial... my first.

Plug In For Trials

March 26, 2019

Ok. Here's an update on my journey in a Phase 1 FIH (First In Human) MM clinical trial that started March 17. March Madness , yikes!

I was told we'd start with a three day stay in the hospital for the first two doses just in case I encountered any troubling reaction to this totally new drug. Well as it turns out I DID experience a troubling reaction and I was in the hospital for seven days. Oh boy!

More on that in just a bit...

First I want to put my plug in for these clinical trials to move new drugs to fight MM through the approval process. Folks we need to have more treatments for MM as we wait on a true cure. We want our MM specialist to have a BIG bag of tricks so we can be there when a cure is found.

My trial is for a new drug that "targets" an aspect of the MM cells that hasn't been tried before now. I'm in part one of the study so there's been only a handful of fellow MM travelers who have been dosed thus far.

This is a unique time for me in my MM journey. My MM is progressing and yet it's likely we have a few months before intervention is absolutely required to head off any MM symptoms. So the researchers can have their way with me and figure out dose tolerances and indeed whether or not the drug can halt MM progression.

As in all clinical trials, patient participation is voluntary. I set three goals that I wanted to achieve while in the trial.

My first goal was to get into a Phase 1 where could help out all of us to launch a totally new drug.

I achieved that. I got in and the research team has already learned from how my body reacted to the drug. Yippee!

My second goal was to learn about the clinical trials... the dos and the donts. I achieved that. I now know quite a lot about clinical trials and from here on out it's likely I'll be in trials, trials and more trials.

I'll be in more trials than Perry Mason (Who? Google him.)

My third goal was to learn about me and grow my ability to rise to the challenges my MM will have for me in the future. I've burned through 4 lines of therapy in six years. The easy "off the shelf" MM solutions are behind me... from here on out I'll be given less proven drugs. The "unknowns" will pepper my MM journey now even more than before and that calls on me to be better at maintaining a positive attitude. This is about trusting God. Already in this trial we've achieved a smidgeon of success towards this goal. I took a pill that has more "unknowns" than "knowns". The first dose whacked me a bit and so I stuck my tongue out at it ... blew it a raspberry and took the second dose.

Which leads me into why it took me seven days to get out of the hospital.

Nothing too serious at all really but the operating tenant of trials is "do no harm" and the docs and researchers are diligent about my safety. So when I had a bout with some pain (short term but on that silly "ouch" scale I reported it as an 8...) then some important count spiked inexplicably. So for my own safety they held me over 'til that count dropped back. (I accused them of just making too much hospital lime Jell-O... they know I love the stuff... and needed me to eat up the excess)

So. Tomorrow I go to the cancer center and get dose #3 and stay the whole day for observation and tests. Dose #4 on Thursday.

Dang! I'll miss The Price is Right two days in a row this week!

Tired

March 29, 2019

Fatigue.

So what's happening in me that is making me so tired? I'm so weak, this morning I didn't even stir my "Fruit on the Bottom" yogurt... I just paddled down from the top!

Tired. Why it just could be those unique molecules of anti-apoptotic protein inhibitor I've been putting in my pie hole. Four doses.

Day 9 of a Phase 1 Clinic trial.

Would you like to learn what we hope is happening in me right now to benefit us all... Readers Digest version?

Easy peezy really.

First a bit of background. Each of our cells has a predetermined set of "shoulds".. what the cell should do in the body... how big the cell should be... Etc.

But we are only going to deal with one cell "should." here: How long that particular cell and cells just like it "should" live. What should the life span of that cell be?

Well the process of regulating cell life span is apoptosis...it's the cell dying at the rate it should.*

And if a cell goes rogue ... wonky... the life span of the cell departs from what it should be.

It's known that the apoptosis of bad guy MM cells is not as it should be. That's the bad news.

But the good news is that apoptosis involves unique proteins that work in concert. Ugh but see that is only when everything is as it "should" be.

*Cells die at widely varied rates. Hair cells are constantly replaced ... that's why we can lose hair cells in chemotherapy... Who cares? They get replaced really fast. For red blood cells it's like 120 days. And, get this… every 11 years or so all the cells in our skeleton... yep... you guessed it... totally replaced. I'm 66 years old and I'm on my sixth skeleton. How cool is that!

And, when things go wonky, the special apoptosis proteins get "overexpressed" on the outer membrane of the wonky myeloma cell. That's good because that makes for a clear "target".

So the smart guy drug research team has selected one of the special apoptosis proteins known to be overexpressed on my MM cells and your MM cells and they have isolated a molecule they figure will target the protein and inhibit it. And then my important MM markers fall into line and I'm singin' Zippity Do Da.

Anti-apoptotic protein inhibitor molecules...

At work in me right now.

Makes me tired just thinking about it.

My oh my what a wonderful day...

Fiddlesticks!

April 2, 2019

Clear the kids from the room I'm droppin the "F" bomb!

FIDDLESTICKS!!!

Late night... adults only... R rated update on me.

Fatigue, yeah. Back ache, yeah. Neuropathy, yeah. Insomnia, some. Fever, nope. Falls, none. Confusion, I'm not sure... hmmmm.

Problem. Oh yeah. There's a problem.

The diarrhea is baaaaaaack. Dang.

Diarrhea. That's how it gets reported in my nifty clinical trial daily diary. Diarrhea. Just diarrhea. La dee da.

But that seemed so... so... understated... each day just noting in passing, diarrhea.

So fourth day I reported it as EDS... Emergency Defecation Situation (that, as you know, differs from the more troubling IWEDS... In Walmart Emergency Defecation Situation.)

And , yabba dabba do, the Imodium tamed it for a few days.

Next episode I reported as my grandmother on the farm called it: "the backyard trots." Dose some Imodium and wait.

Success. Life is good.

I so hope I'm past this side effect of the new drug I'm on. Because from here on out the terms for "it" get ugly. Real ugly. Yep next I report it as THS... and I so do NOT want to do that.

Number 22

April 14, 2019 at 11:43 AM

Ok fellow MM travelers for today I have for us a number and a question.

The number is 22.

And the question? Well, I'll get to that.

But first about that number 22. That for me is way up from just a month ago when it was probably half that.

Well, 22 is the number of pill bottles I'm currently rotating through on my daily quest to feel just ok and get vertical .

Lemme see, there's two for diarrhea ...one for calcium... one for vitamin D... a stool softener... an antibiotic... Metamucil fiber... acyclovir anti-viral... choice of three over the counter pain relievers... choice of three dangerously potent prescription pain relievers... gabapentin for neuropathy... three for nausea (take your pick, Bruce, none of them will work anyway... Zofran… Compazine... Ativan…) oh, and two to have a go at altering my mood including that crap Xanax which comes in a child proof bottle with the cracked lid from me tossing it against the wall and I didn't need it anyway MY MOOD IS FINE!!! JUST FINE. NOW LEAVE ME ALONE!!!

Whew!

Oh the question. Yeah right.

The one bottle says "for breakthrough pain."

Where is my breakthrough? Is that like a bone? I hurt all over but I just don't know where my "breakthrough" even is. Is "breakthrough" slang for something? You know like "Charlie horse" means a cramp.

At The Cancer Center

April 16, 2019 at 6:00 PM

Update:

Long day at the Cancer Center

My MM doc (who is excellent BTW) was very ready to remove me from the trial today but I pleaded with him to wait until end of day tomorrow. He is not optimistic that the my Lambda Light chain marker number will be down. We get that number tomorrow sometime.**

** 5 weeks ago at the start of the trial that # was 40...two weeks ago there was no good news... the number jacked to 69... So we need to see that the trial drug is working on me so I don't continue to see evidence of progressing mm. We need to see a pullback in that number or it's bye bye Bruce from the clinical trial.

The back thingy I've got is the MM... Either a softened, compressed vertebrae (inject plastic) or a glump of myeloma activity rubbing onto a nerve Eeeeeee oww (radiation treatment).

They took X-rays today and will do MRIs tomorrow evening. I asked to go ahead with the bone marrow biopsy tomorrow regardless and take two more doses of the trial drug as we wait.

Dang, don't we all just love all the waiting?

He will decide once we see the LLC # but if it's bad we will start a new somephin somephin treatment scheme hopefully on Thursday.

So we wait for that hugely important LLC marker number.

Queue the Jeopardy game show waiting song:

...dump da dump dump dump... dump... dump... dump

The important questions though really are: Did I get free parking? Was the nurse prac really hitting on me? Did I get nicked for a $45 copay?

Answers: Of course. Of course NOT, DOH!... and nope, so we ordered Chinese delivery dinners to celebrate. Ha!

Ratted Myself Out

April 16, 2019 at 9:42 AM

So yesterday I ratted myself out to my MM specialist. Back pain. Ouch! Well, to be honest, OUCH!!!

Later the nurse prac calls me back and I'm thinkin "YES!" because I've suspected for a while now that she's hot for me...

Ahem. Well, no such luck.

The doc wants to see me immediately to get to the bottom of my back. Huh? What?

Bottom line is I'll miss today's The Price is Right attending to this pesky incurable cancer and the debilitating whoa diggy in my spine. Dang!

My friend Michael will do the livery service thing because I'm told I shouldn't drive myself... something about having vision in just one eye combined with being dosed with opioid pain meds combined with all those jerks in the way on MY ROAD... HEY!! GET A MOVE ON OR MOVE OUT OF MY WAY!!!

Prayers that this back thingy isn't going to affect me continuing in the clinical trial. There's no evidence yet... it's been just 4 weeks for me in the trial... that the trial drug is knocking back my progressing MM. And now there's this "What? Huh?" with my back.

Lots of chin scratch by the doc and the trial sponsor today.

Folks we need me IN this trial so they learn more about this new drug for us in the future and that takes time.

So I'm off to see the white coats and sweet talk the receptionist.

"Co Pay??? $45??? Oh that can't be right..."

"Yes and please validate this 100% free parking chit I get because I'm poor and disabled and half blind and over 65 and I have cancer and I'm in a clinical trial.....

Not to mention the major who-ha wedged between my vertebrae "

Wince. Grimace. Both elbows on the counter. Bite the lower lip.

Silently just whisper the word:

"Please."

Works every time.

Clinical Trial Update

April 19, 2019 at 6:47 PM

Clinical trial update:

I have exciting news!

Thanks to your prayers and encouragements we remained in the trial this week... long enough to see genuine results. Yep yep and , boy howdy that means ole MM has been knocked back by this brand new idea for a drug.

What a marvelous week in MMville. On Tuesday the doc was all ready to pull me from the trial because, after 4 weeks, we'd seen no evidence that the stuff was working. In fact I started in the trial at Lambda Light chain of 40... after three weeks that had risen to 69. Whoops!

And on Tuesday I'd ratted myself out and reported that whoa diggy on my back.

But we were allowed just one more day and another LLC test and an MRI to figure out the whoa diggy thingy.

Well on Wednesday we get the LLC results... and... get this folks, it had FALLEN to 50! That number had been advancing in me since September 2018.

(Ahem, (he says under his breath) yeah and we go for that ridiculously noisy MRI imaging which is the bad news but this update is about our GOOD NEWS, eh?)

Next day... MORE good news. Another LLC test... this time 22!!

From 69 to 22 folks and no other MM drug is involved . It's a single agent test.

Folks we did it. Stayed in the Phase 1 trial of this new apoptotic protein inhibitor targeting MCL-1. And the stuff WORKED!

Good Friday indeed, Praise God.

Oh yeah. Now for the "bad news" but not really... there is no bad news...we found a new MM solution perhaps, right?

Well that whoa diggy on my back needs radiation treatment immediately and the trial sponsors are doing some "push back" on me continuing in the trial because I'll be getting radiation treatments.

Fiddlesticks!

But celebrate your part in the success side of this trial. We stayed in, group, and the stuff worked. Ha!

Hot diggity dog!

Worry

April 23 at 3:56 AM

Ah well. Can't sleep. So I'll muse myself into dreamland.

Subject? Well, I pick the subject of what is, for me, a personal goal to do better at each day on my MM journey.

Worry.

(I don't mean my goal is to be a better worrier... my goal is to not worry at all. Step aside Alfred E. Neuman!... who?... Google his quote.)

It's not uncommon to see here in an MM group a posting of someone's lab numbers and then the question "Should I be worried."

I'll spout that no matter the number it never makes much sense to worry at it. I'll wag a knowing finger and proclaim "Don't worry. The cancer doesn't even know if you worry about it."

And in my best Nancy Reagan I'll nag "Just say no!" to worrying.

And I do a rather fine job most of the time at not stepping on the rake of worry that's ALWAYS right there in my path. Go that way and WHACK! right between the eyes and things go from "troubling" to genuine wasteful worrying.

A person wiser than me (What's that... Huh?... who be wiser than you , Bruce?)... yeah, a person wiser than me... compared worrying to being bullied.

Yeah. Treat worry like a bully.

Ignore it, ok. Laugh at it, ok, yeah that's good. I like a good laugh.

Just don't take that path where you run into worry. Just like you took another way home from elementary school to avoid a bully, if the lab numbers lead to worry, take the road less travelled and avoid the numbers game today.

Easier said than done? Perhaps.

What if I don't get my numbers and there's something bad in there and I don't know about it soon enough to smear some worry on it?

Or worse , what if the number is bad and I don't worry about at all and I sleep just fine because I missed seeing it and I didn't worry and tell the dog how worried I am about my immunoglobulin stats.

I'm worried that this whole "don't worry" thing is just some internet scam and I'll get phished and my identity will be thieved.

Hmmmmmm.

I'm sleepy now. No worries.

Comments:

"You're so cute."

"Love your outlook on life…"

"Uh I'm worried that I don't worry about my MM. Just another pebble in the rocky road of my life! If I get anxious I have an all-natural herb that helps immensely!)."

"I choose not to worry about the things over which I have no control – because worrying about them will make no difference. Over the things I have control, I choose not to worry, but instead do the best that I can with no regrets. I'm too busy trying to live the most each day to have time or energy to worry…"

"Bruce, you have had a fantastic full filling life, don't let this thing MM change your life, yes we do have some hiccups along the way but life is still great, every day brings

with it new experiences that we may never of had if we didn't have MM.

And you're right don't worry !!!

Cherish everyday :-)))) and keep smiling."

"The Pomallist alarm I set on my iPod plays: "Don't Worry, Be Happy". I mentioned to my visiting brother-in-law that I've had that song on there for two years now and maybe should change it. He said "Why? It's a good reminder!" Being happy is what I do best!!

Clinical Trial Update

April 26 at 7:01 PM

Clinical Trial Update:

Pee Wee's Great Adventure Part Deux.

Well, I was allowed to stay in the trial and take two more doses and use up one more of my just ordered from Amazon vomit bags (Product review alert! Search "sick sack" and get the blue ones with the extra wide mouth. Fancy!)

And with the two doses of trial drug comes two (pardon the term) runs of THS which is like diarrhea only louder.

I've an appointment with the radiologist dude on Monday but I've read my MRI and well folks it's more than a whoa diggy on my back. This one qualifies as a genuine who ha!

Yep it's a lesion that extends into the left lateral recess with severe compression of the left L3 nerve root. What? Huh?

Boy howdy and ouch!

(Here's a hint. The really good pills for back pain ... right on the bottle... have an icon of a little car skidding dangerously out of control. Yep. Dem babies work!)

From what they tell me it looks like I'll get daily radiation and while that's going on they will stop the trial drug doses and that means I'm way over stocked in blue roundmouth disposable vomit bags.

As for the back who ha, I'm dosed with the "may cause dizziness" pill and I'm putting on my best "Grandpa Amos McCoy" hitch in the git along jig when I walk.

(Go to YouTube for Grandpa Amos McCoy...that's me now. "Papina the barn is on fire! Papina!")

Oh and the really good news is that I look legit getting out of the car at the Dollar Store. I'm clearly somebody that needs that handicap tag now.

Gee if only the Dollar Store sold my favorite brand of sick sacks. Alas.

Comments:

"I don't remember Walter Brennan being this funny! Keep fighting the good fight."

"Omg, I'm so sorry to hear that this is your trial of the moment, but boy, I love the way you tell it! Sending you positive thoughts!"

"Thank you for keeping us updated. In my prayers. Thx for the laughs also."

"Bruce Morton, I'm so sorry for what you're dealing with. I'm glad you were able to get two more doses of the trial drug. From what I remember, it was working for you. I hope the radiation works well and works quickly to resolve the issues you're having with your back. Thank you for updating and for sharing your incredible sense of humor. You are an inspiration!"

"Keep up the good fight Bruce, the world needs your sense of humor. Big hugs and many prayers for a quick recovery."

"Bruce you are amazing. Thank you for sharing your story with us I should say your stories."

"Love you are laughing! that is the best medicine. Your posts make me laugh. Stay strong and keep your sense of humor. You lighten many of us. …for a great outcome. Thanks again."

"I'm sorry that I always laugh at your writings... you just have such a wonderful sense of humor that comes out in your writing. Seriously Bruce Morton I'm praying for

you and this journey you are on. God bless and keep you!"

"Glad you can still find the humor in all this.."

"Keep the writing coming and I am glad you can stay in the trial! You are in my prayers- get rid of that lesion!"

"Hang in there Bruce Morton!! Thinking about you often!! Thanks for the post."

"I'm really sorry about the clinical trial and the lesion/back pain... but I have to tell you that I think you're awesome."

Vivid Dream

April 30, 2019 at 2:12 AM

Right. This day begins with a VERY vivid dream... in COLOR.

All goes well in the dream because I scored a "punch" in my "have you ever been to a ________ist" punchcard .

It's a punch card.

I get to punch out "radiologist." Yippee.

(Previously punched along my MM journey ...and these are all TRUE!... are generalist, hematologist, then thankfully my current hematology-oncologist.

Punched.

Then there was the urologist with absolutely NO sense of humor and she referred me to the psychiatrist. Which got me referred to the psychologist, who had an immediate dislike of me.

Punched.

Kidney stone. Eeeeee is for Emergency Room...

Nephrologist.

Ophthalmologist and his pal the Otolaryngologist surgeon that saved one eye (Yay!) but sadly we lost the other eye. (Drat!)

Cardiologist who cared deeply about my heart (which is a whole lot more than I can say about my second wife, by golly!) All punched .

Dermatologist... itchy scratchy and punchy.

Pulmonologist. Punched.

Neurologist. Punched.

Not punched gynecologist.

Not punched proctologist **

Dream NOT over.

Back pain gets REAL. Worse and real. Opioids. Radiation sessions.

We are off to the Cancer Center... I'm too drugged up to drive... past the construction of the new location for my eye doctor...

"Look... it's a site for sore eyes"

I quip.

(I apologize. That joke is SO PAST it's "Use By____" date. Ugh. OLD! Sorry.)

We arrive at the FRONT of the RADIOLOGY Building and I think "Morton, you idiot. This is wrong. So very wrong." And in the dream we drive around to the BACK door and , you betcha, there's my BACK doctor .

Smug am I.

Ok the radiationist asks me about my pain.

Location. Level. (on that annoying pain chart) .

Well then he tells me that in addition to the who ha on the L3 there's a smaller but troubling "my oh my" at S2. (Hmmm. I'm thinking: "Two - fer" price break ?)

The procedure for me is that they will pass the radiation (He said "X-ray" but, is that true?) through the area that has the myeloma activity.

The dream jumps, I mean JUMPS to that laser ray scene in "Goldfinger"... James Bond strapped to the table.

Bzzzz Bzzzz goes the laser.

Bzzzzz Bzzzzz .

Pointed right at his L3 and his S2

Ok back from dreamland. The realities of our MMville life. My first treatment is on Wednesday for ten total sessions. For now the plan is for me to remain in the trial study but while getting radiation they will temporarily stop the doses of the trial drug.

So. We want the radiation treatments to be over quickly so that we can get back to the clinical trial.

Yep. Yep.

** In the dream, that leaves me alone with only the proctologist. Yikes!

(Don't be squeamish I've read this entire post and you'll do fine.)

In the dream the scene is my initial appointment with the dream proctologist. (Oxymoron?)

So the nurse politely says

"Welcome Mr. Morton, you can sit right there . It will be just a short wait for Doctor Schoertwhayte."

I squawk:

"WHAT!!! SIT for a SHORT WAIT!!!

If I could SIT I wouldn't even be here! You stupid NAZI."

I hate Dex days.

I storm out, nicking a peppermint as I leave.

In my dream I don't see Dr. Schoertwhayte but instead get a referral to another proctologist from my friends Ben and Ilene. The Dovers. Nice couple. Their guy is Dr. Lukasia. Ben though calls Dr. Lukasia "Cool Hand Luke? Hmmmmmmm.

BONUS JOKE ALERT! In the above there sits a hidden har har. No additional charge and we may get a bonus smile from ya.

Comments:

"Bruce.......you always brighten my day with your antics ☺ I hope the radiation works and gives you some pain relief!!! Take Care"

"If we had a "make a wish" thing and could meet any other patient, you'd be my first choice! Even my husband is getting tired of hearing about your stories. But your sense of humor is worth a thousand pictures and you keep me chuckling even on the days I want to throw things!"

"Ditto that!! He needs to do a "My Myeloma Journey" presentation at one of those conference thingys!!"

"Awesome sense of humor. I love the punch card concept. I think you could compile these posts into a book! Thank you for the smiles. Wishing you much success with the radiation and the trial. ☺"

"God Bless you my friend and may HE wrap you in his arms and get you through this day to day thing called MM Life!"

"Bruce, I hope the radiation helps and is over soon. I know you are ready to get back to the trial. I am so grateful for your sense of humor. You have been on such a difficult road and faced it with humor. I pray

that God blesses you with more humor and less pain."

"You are awesome Bruce. Hope the best for you."

"Whoa! A Very vivid dream. You need to start writing short screen plays. ☺"

"My friend, your sense of humor, in such troubling times, gives us all a special gift and shines a light on your beautiful spirit. Thank you for keeping me in laughs as you explore the unknown for all of us...❤"

Radiation

May 1, 2019 at 12:58 PM

First of ten radiation sessions. Da da done.

Yesterday was mapping where the nurse had me drop my britches so she could cop a glance at my junk and then use a sharpee to mark my belly area that serves as a target. The shape is roughly like Indiana and my navel (inny) is Terre Haute.

Today I'm laid out and ready.

"Ask me how long I've had my weak back." Says I to the nurse. She does and I say "Since about a week back!!" Nothin. Not even a grin.

They soothe you with the music of your choice.

Wow!

"Anything by RAY Charles." Says I to the nurse. Again nothin. I POINT to the machine... RAYS... RAY Charles... get it?... Crickets…

Buzz goes the machine around me. And just that fast it's over and it takes three techs to sit me up but they get it done. Ooooeeee!

Now I'm home. Ray Charles on Pandora and just a little itch right near Evansville ...

Comments:

*"Bruce Morton, in the spirit of the need for humor with this really crappy b*tch of a disease, healthcare workers are under terrific pressure, the toll on them is enormous as medical treatment is a full-on business with overworked individuals, short-staffed a lot of the time and big corporations that don't really gave a damn except for the bottom line. It is so hard to always keep a smile on our faces and our humor in check. I agree that unfriendly, grouchy nurses are no fun, but I have to somewhat defend my colleagues as I see it day in and day out. Most important Bruce Morton is for you to keep your sense of humor going and know that this group loves it. We'll provide for you what the grouchy nurse did not. ☺*

From the editor:

"I love em all. A few sessions ago at my MM specialist two of the nurses gave me the ultimate compliment . One said to the other "He... (Bruce) is my favorite patient." And the other nurse agrees with a thumbs up! And we all laugh together.

And we will laugh together tomorrow when she delivers the news that my light chain number just doubled (I'm seeing the online chart of my blood draw from yesterday... I'll get the call tomorrow)...

doubled in two weeks . Yeah. That's bad. And what a tough job to have to deliver that sort of news to patients."

"I hate it when they don't laugh!! But at mayo, they kept telling me I was the funniest patient they ever had... I loved that they were cool... ☺!!"

"you always crack me up! Keep writing for us, pleeeese. ☺"

"Love the wise cracks!! Hope you are feeling a bit better ❤"

I hate it when they don't laugh!! But at mayo, they kept telling me I was the funniest patient they ever had.. I loved that they were cool...😂!!

✈you always crack me up! Keep writing for us, pleeeese.😂😂

Love the wise cracks!! Hope you are feeling a bit better ❤

Evansville is no paradise either.

Uggggg I took 10 also. Probably MM worst treatment for me

You sure make it easier for lots of us to hang tough day by day, by putting smiles on our faces! Keep it up Bruce!!! Wishes for healing for all as we maneuver the nasties.

Where is her humor?? I was a therapy tech. I always joked

Wth!! That nurse needs an attitude adjustment ! I mean you showed her you junk !! Lol. I had BMB today and had 3 of the hottest guys in radiology with their hands all over my body.

Drop her one of those good pills. She'll be smilin fer miles. (Ahem, of course this is a joke!)

When I had a cardiac MRI a couple years ago, the tech gave me headphones and asked my choice in music. When I asked about classic rock, she replied "You mean like from the 90s?"

Thankful

May 5, 2019

Thankful.

Today we place full importance on being thankful.

Thankful for the gift of another day. Another chance to laugh. Another chance to be grateful to all the people who help us along the way on our MM journey.

(People Who Need People... how's that go? You know that singer with the incredible voice....)

Today. Ha! I got a laugh... a true, honest to goodness, out loud laugh from that nurse that was grumpy (not really, she's just "all business "and we know it's never "all business" with me, eh?)

It wasn't a joke that got her today. My jokes were falling flat.

But see I'm in for radiation on a "who ha" on my back and they "map" onto my belly a target with a

Sharpee pen. It's a genuine "x marks the spot" Sharpee mark that I was warned not to wash off.

But they didn't warn me about additional marks.

So I drew Nurse Grumpy...with my own Sharpee... a big "Smiley Face" right on a spare square of the ole tum tum. Ha! "Gotcha" says I. Now we are best buds.

It took me three days but I got her to laugh. Ha! Thankful indeed. (Though now it's gonna take me four days to scrub that Sharpee Smiley Face off my belly.)

I'm thankful for that huge radiation machine that is x-raying my insides. Thankful that the pain seems to be a bit less.

Thankful the doc is keeping a close watch on my LLC count because it's on the rise again.... doubled in just two weeks. Thankful I'm technically still in the clinical trial and hopeful I'll be treated again with the trial drug (it was working two weeks ago nicely against my MM but we had to interrupt that for the radiation treatments).

Thankful that two friends came by today to tend to me. Fill my water bowl. Scold me. Laugh with me.

Thankful, yes I am. Ha!

Comments:

"It makes me happy that you got her to laugh today. Thankful. I'm thankful you are my friend. I'm thankful that you are feeling a little less pain. I'm thankful for your posts, and I know in my heart that what you are going through is much harder than what you let on. Sorry I've been incommunicado. Hoping you feel up to chatting this weekend. ❤"

"You bring me up Bruce, even on my bad days. Keep posting. ☺"

"I love your sense of humor!"

"Proverbs 17:22 – 'A merry heart doeth good like a medicine: but a broken spirit drieth the bones.'"

Praying they can give you needed help! God's got you!❤☺"

"Bruce Morton, We're thankful for YOU for being such an inspiration to the rest of us—for reminding us to be thankful in uncertain circumstances and for sharing your wonderful sense of humor."

"Oh Bruce, you made me snort soda out of my nose! Thank you. I haven't

laughed that hard in a long time!"

"Please keep posting they are amazing. Yes be thankful. I met a fellow warrior on Wed that was so negative. Now I am not judging she is newly diagnosed and is obviously having a very hard time with it. I will try to be a positive role model and Bruce postings like you do are a way for me to tap into my positivity.

Mission Impossible

May 7, 2019

About a year ago now I set out on a mission.

Mission Impossible…

Queue the music.

Dump. Dump. Dump-Dump

Dump. Dump

Da da da.... da da da...

da Dump.

I took on the mission to change my attitude about all things. To change my default setting in life to: Smile.

To swipe the words and actions right from the classic Charlie Chaplin song: Just Smile... done best I think by Nat King Cole.

My plan was to fully infest this "new normal" life with smiles.

Sure we smile when the marker numbers are good, but what if they aren't? Well phooey anyway there's not been a marker number yet that's so important that I can't push back on it with a smile. I can't change the number but I can change how I react.

Though my heart is weary, eh?

So I've been workin this game and I can say that yeah... so far... I'm pulling it off pretty darn offer. Yep. yep. And ha ha.

A few things along the way have upset me but after a bit... I reset... find the dog... get a proper dose of "smile... just smile" from the pooch. Remember the mission.

Default setting: smile

New normal: more smiles

Kick it up a notch, Emeril: Laugh out loud!

And,

Bam!

Somehow I just feel better.

(Right now I've lots to smile about... daily radiation treatment from my new best friend nurse... plenty of opportunity for more oxy... Ha!... step aside back pain...

And dog Ellie has me laughing out loud at my wigglely walk.)

Yeah.

Just Smile... give it a try!

Then kick it up a notch and laugh out loud.

Comments:

You remind me of a friend of mine going through chemo for breast cancer. She is a firecracker that stays happy go lucky. Although she does have her bad days and can admit it. She finds that reset button and smiles and sings again.

😁😁💪💪. *Laughter IS the best medicine. And incredible friends..... those personally know and not ! Thank you Bruce my friend ! Mucho grande love.*

You're so awesome!! Thanks for sharing. 😁😁😁

It amazes me how much smiling at others can change my attitude. I've also found that little acts of kindness, as well as complimenting others, can boost my mood.

Good advice for us all! I like the "reset" thought, too.

smiles to you, Bruce, ☺ *a very nice reminder. Thank you.* ❤

When I was diagnosed I realized there were many things that were out of my control but I could control my attitude and disposition. I've decided to be thankful for all I have instead of complaining about problems. It certainly has helped me having a positive attitude.

Piddlin Puny

May 10, 2019

Myeloma Fatigue....

An all over, deep fatigue that sets in as part of our MM journey.

Either the disease itself or the meds they pump into us. The more they pump in the less productivity we pump out. Ugh. Sigh. Groan.

Well I'm just now getting introduced to fatigue from radiation treatment for the tumor that's decided to take up residence on my L3 vertebrae. See, I'm getting a total of ten radiation treatments and by the third the fatigue was getting annoying. By the sixth treatment I was horizontal most all of each day and night. Lots of Cheetos crumbs in the bedding. Empty Ensure bottles on the nightstand.

So last night I called in reinforcements and arranged for my caregiver sister, Karen to livery me to treatment number eight this morning. I was simply too tired. It wasn't safe for me to be trying to drive myself.

Fatigue from multiple myeloma. Or the chemo treatments or the radiation treatments.

Have you ever tried to explain to a healthy person what it's like to experience multiple myeloma fatigue?

No word or phrase does justice to how tired we get.

Tired isn't enough of a word for it. Super tired. Deeply tired. Nah.

Slight... I feel "slight" today... Ugh well, NO.

Spent. Or "just plain SPENT." Mmmm that's closer.

Plum tuckered out. That's too regional... that's only right for here in the Ozarks.

One doc said to me once "on the days that you are "puny".

"Puny". Yeah puny. Yeah maybe puny.

But with myeloma fatigue you are so wrapped in nothing... so deep in a bucket of pooped, puny is just too big of a word.

Puny is chocked full of energy placed up beside myeloma fatigue.

So, what says "less" than puny?

Minor puny? Itsy bitsy puny? Nano puny? Paultry puny? Minuscule puny?

Yeah I guess all those work.

But after treatment eight I'm gonna go with...

wait for it...

Piddling Puny

Today in MMville Bruce is Piddling Puny.

Same jammies. Day number three and counting.

He lets the dog in and goes back to bed.

And so it goes. And so it goes.

Comments:

I had an anti-fatigue button I wore 20 years ago during my induction therapy. That was the worst side effect of my chemo. But it worked, and I am still here. There is a light at the end of the tunnel. Hang in there, Bruce.

I was feeling peppy enough this morning that after picking up a prescription at Walgreens I asked my wife to detour past Lowe's as I felt I might pick up a few annuals to fill in a bare area in my garden.

Hard to push through! One step at a time is all you can do!

I remember sitting on the edge of my bed getting dressed and staring at my dresser three feet away and asking myself....do I really need a bra today?? No, no I do not. Yes, fatigue from the depths of a dark chasm

You're absolutely right about how a healthy person doesn't understand MM tired! Bruce you can get through these last radiation treatments! You've got to get your humor back👆❤.

Praying for you 🙏

Hang in there. Following ❤

Year 19 this weekend 2 asct now dara

Garbanzo Bean

May 12, 2019

Tumor.

This new one is bigger than a garbanzo bean yet smaller than a peach pit.

First doc said it's a tumor (though I believe the more proper name for it when it's from MM is plasmacytoma but that has too many letters and I'm old, so, tumor.) from the MM... on my sternum... won't get radiation treatment because there's no pain (we'll see about that)...

It can be officially counted as a tumor so for those keeping count that's two tumors discovered on/in me in the last month... just one more and I score a tumor hat trick. However, if I can make it til June 1 with no new "who ha's" the official "uh oh" counter resets and we start all over.

Hee hee this time my BFF nurse prac called to scold me: "YOU didn't tell me you have a plasmacytoma!"

I'm learning proper tumor protocol . See, the nurse prac in charge has first dibs on any new tumor discoveries.

So, these are my first tumors and I simply did not know tumor protocol. To clarify: Tell the nurse prac of ANY new lump, mass, hard spot, tender area, or "it hurts when I push there". Be prepared to describe the size: BB, green pea, garbanzo bean, peach pit, etc.

Be prepared to know how long it's been there.

So I am to appear in person on Tuesday to tell my tumor tale to my MM specialist. In my defense, truly, it doesn't hurt... at all. And, it... the tumor... is barely visible. You gotta look REALLY long and hard at my necked chest to notice anything untowards.

I'll stop right here and fess up that I'm NOT in the habit of doing a visual check of necked Bruce. Ugh. Gasp!

But, hey I wouldn't be me without all the lumps and divots. It's those imperfections that make me so loveable and huggable.

So. Another unpleasant task for the MM traveler.

Check yourself regularly for any changes ... don't simply rely on "new pain". Or have a close partner or homeless person give you the once over every so often.

Then call the nurse prac...they have first dibs.

(And , yeah , don't call it a tumor , it's a plasmacytoma , Yadda yadda...

Comments:

They get better and better Bruce! Your stories (although true) are educational, inspiring, and funny. 🙈😂. Thank you for sharing and giving us more to be aware of. Now when is the "MM Book for Dummies" coming out? 😀💪

Bruce Morton you may be corny or dry humor "as some would say" but you are a breath of fresh air and you keep it real from only your eyes! 😀😂. I love it! When I hear your stories it reminds me of my friend and his saying "Grinding My Life Away". Keep Grinding my friend! 💪

I get them on and around my rib cage. Mine was extremely painful. Radiation was a significant relief.

From an old ICU nurse, the "oma" at the end of plasmacytoma means tumor so you go right ahead and call it a tumor. If somebody asks what kind, you can wow them with more knowledge. I'm glad you aren't in any pain.

Bruce Morton exactly. I try to be grateful. I have a lot to be thankful for.

Why are they always described using food references?

I asked my doctor that exact question. My understanding is that a lesion is used to describe a compromise in the bone material, holes, softness, weakness, etc. A plasmacytoma or tumor is an additional growth. When she used the word lesion while speaking about my plasmacytoma I inquired again, and she said the plasmacytoma could infiltrate the bone at which time it causes a lesion.

"Visual checks of naked Bruce"....ROFL.

I think I love you! Keep smiling and thanks for sharing

Love this post. Allison is my oncology nurse, after any biopsy I asked Did you send that to Allison?

Bruce, as always your wit is so appreciated. I am so sorry you have to endure yet another crazy thing going on with your body. Hang in there!

Here, Lucky

May 13, 2019

To start your day.

(Don't be alarmed this is all in jest ...I'm fine tucked safely under my blue blankie with the pretty fish prints. DO NOT CALL 911.)

I've written my own "Lost Person" flyer and I'll man my staple gun and "post" the old fashion way .

LOST MAN.

Last seen wearing white T shirt with Maroon Crossed Ribbon. Plaid jammy bottoms.

Wanders off. Chemo brain...forgets where home is.

Left his medications. LOTS of medications!

Grey scruffy hair and beard. Splotchy skin.

Slooooooow gate and crookedy stance.

Friendly and likes Metamucil wafers as a treat to coax him.

Lovable and huggable disposition.

Mostly housebroken discounting the occasional "accident " . Piddles . (Sorry full and sad afterwards).

NOT good with children or cats.

Cancer Bows to a Smile

Tumor on the back

Tumor on the front

Totally blind in one eye

Answers to name "Lucky"

(If you see him just offer Metamucil wafer cookies and he'll come right to you.)

Comments:

I have been on this trip since 2014. I have asked God to keep my sense of humor through it all. I try to put a smile on all the faces of the Drs. and nurses as well as other patients I meet. I do all the poor pitiful me behind a "oak tree" but when I come out, it is with a smile. Thanks so much for being that person that brings a smile to those that need it.

I agree, we need to Keep our sense of humor through our journey.

I love you posts they make me smile

Bruce, thanks for making my day. How you can have such a wonderful sense of humor in dealing with all this, I do not know. You are such a blessing to all who read your posts. You definitely bless my heart with each one.

My family think I'm nuts! But you topped that xxxxxxxxxx excellent, best wishes fellow nutter x

Bruce - you made my day! Keep that sense of humor as it will carry you (and us) thru.

You are so hysterical!

Dropped From The Trial

May 14, 2019

Clinical Trial Update…

I have been dropped as a participant in the Phase 1 Trial for the new protein inhibitor type drug. I was one of 90 participants.

(Although the new drug showed promise with me my mm returned and is progressing. My dose level in the trial was locked in so we had to pull me out of the study to treat me with some other approach.)

The trial continues and everyone is hopeful the drug... it's so new they'd not even given it a name... will continue through the process and eventually come to market as an FDA approved treatment for MM.

I again want encourage all who can to participate in clinical trials. Our MM teams need more treatment options so that each of us is around when that elusive cure for MM is released.

Comments:

Bummer... best to move on to another treatment at this point. Thanks for participating in the trial.

I am sorry sorry Bruce! I am positive that there wil be mother one that can help you even better. Keep strong don't get discouraged and I am sending prayers

😱 *Are you in touch with Spark Cures? They work to help people find clinical trials and are really kind people.*

Sorry it didn't work out for you Bruce. Hope your team has something better for you now. I just had third treatment of my clinical trial today with Selinexor/Kyprolis, and Dex. Got along fine with it last week taking anti nausea pills every six hours for four days. M/M seems to be on the run so far.

So sorry this did not work out. My prayers are with you for another solution.

Now it's Bendamustine

May 17, 2019

My MM specialist has changed my treatment therapy to Bendamustine (Monday and Tuesday infusions) combo with daily M-Th Prednisone. (Then three weeks off... then start again.)

Does anyone have any experience with this regimen? Side effects? How long did you stay on this combo? Was it used as a "bridge" to a next therapy?

Thanks.

Comments:

no experience with that therapy but just want to wish you the best of luck. We are all rooting for you!

No experience, but I hope things work out positive for you-holding positive thoughts for you

Never heard of it. Something new?

No experience with that one

I had that when I was d hospitalized at diagnosis in October 2014...but in was on morphine so I remember nothing.... sorry I can't answer your question.

No experience. What is your actual diagnosis? It's apparently mostly used to treat non-Hodgkins Lymphoma.

Can I inquire as to how old you are and which other therapies you've used? I want to say this is related to "mustard gas". I'd have to guess you've tried other therapies?

Infusion Day

May 19, 2019

Well it has been a while since last they covered me with that soothing warm blanky at the infusion lounge.

(It was last May when I took the red wagon ride with the first responders to the ER. "No more Kyprolis for YOU")

But tomorrow is Infusion Day again...Yay!

Sung to the tune of "Yesterday"

"Infusion Day"

Infusion Day

Good times good times are a vein away

Bring me that free Milky Way

Oh I'll be there ...

Infusion Day

Suddenly

I have doubled in my LLC

Plasma bag hanging over me

Infusion Day came sudd-en-ly

Why be-cause I'm sick, or they say

I say:

"I don't know."

"I'll be strong."

Infusion day ay ay

Infusion Day

Chills and steroids go away

Where is my free Milky Way

Oh I believe

Infusion Day

Mmm...mm...mm..mm..mm

Mm..mm

I'll dose with prednisone first then it's toes up for the two hour infusion of relatively uncommon (or at least out of fashion) drug Bendamustine. This drug is PERFECT for me at this juncture of my mm journey. (INSERT HERE REASON WHY BENDA IS SO PERFECT... beats the heck outta me ???).

This drug is so nice I get it TWICE. So Tuesday it's straight back to be back on my back for more. Plus more pred.

Then just the Pred on Wednesday and Thursday.

After which we wait, knowing that my LLC (Lambda Light chain) marker, which is all jacked up right now, will drop drop drop. My platelets, whites and hemoglobin will come home to roost in normal range . And that slightly right-side-of-center tumor on my chest will be off to Never, Never Land. (And the Tooth Fairy is on the way too I'll betcha! Really though... it's all good ... Angels watching over me, eh.)

Tomorrow is familiar territory, eh…

"Bruce Morton... labs... infusion... no port... arm draw..."

"Of course I remember my date of birth!" Ugh ..."

"What? $45 co-pay??... That can't be right!"

"Free parking... I get free parking, right?"

"And snacks... Milky Way and CheezIts, right?"

"Warm blanky please. Let's do the left arm today and save the right for tomorrow."

And so it goes... And so it goes…

Comments:

Wishing you bits of happiness wherever you can find it. I really liked your song today!

I strongly recommend you publish your Facebook musing in a book.

my best wishes to you . Ask for a Milky Way

Thanks for the chuckle!

So clever and creative!

You've made my day ------ AGAIN

Love it. You've made my day. Hope everything goes well 😱

Thanks for the entertainment. I needed that. Good luck.

Praying for positive outcome and good luck MM warriors!

my best wishes to you. I always look for your posts

Bruce, I totally enjoyed the new song - you are not only very humorous but also very creative. O pray that this protocol does what it is supposed to do and that you feel better. I agree with the others that you should publish your musings. It would definitely help others be able to enjoy your sense of humor and be able to look beyond themselves to something that might brighten their day

Love this post!

Love your upbeat attitude Bruce! My infusion room doesn't give Milky Way bars or CheeseIts. ☹ You are a lucky guy!

I only wish it wasnt foremost in my mind all the time. Im reading Grisham novels that Ive missed for relaxation and diversion

Good luck to you Bruce! I've never known anyone with so much humor and positivity going into difficult circumstances! You crack me up. Always.

Pull My Finger

May 22, 2019 at 6:02 AM

New treatment therapy update…

Monday was the first infusion of chemo drug Bendamustine... repeated on Tuesday... combo with high doses of steroid prednisone.

Not much info to be found about this scheme as a MM strategy though my infusion nurse knew it well as a lymphoma drug.

(She saw Bendamustine on the order and I swear her face was awash with a sort of "ugh oh" and "what's that smell?" look.)

So I googled Bendamustine and deep into the search found that the words "benda de mustine" translated means "pull my finger"

After that very first infusion on Monday I was introduced to how Bendamustine came to be known as the "pull my finger" drug.

Yikes, boys and girls OMG. The flatulence released from this therapy is incredible.

Day two:

I sound like a polka band in rehearsal tuning the tubas.

Walking. Just walking and it's ratta tat tat!

That scene in Blazing Saddles. The Campfire. The Beans. Think THAT scene ON STEROIDS.

That's me.

The dog, Ellie, has lost all respect for me. She won't invite any of her friends over ever again.

Plus I'm still recovering from the nifty 10 radiation treatments that got sprayed at the tumor on my L3.

Fatigue. Weak. There's not a food package I don't struggle to open. Even my handy Lunchables has me heading for the scissors.

Getting INTO bed is my version of the Fosbury Flop (google him).

Getting OUT of bed...Ha!

I'm too weak to stand right up and truth be told I really could use a helper.

My solution until my strength returns is a combination FLING mixed with FLAIL ... but don't forget the Bendamustine.

So it's push up with the right arm... kick lightly with the left leg... bounce... fart... push harder... kick... bounce... push up and…

Ya Yes! He is up!!!

Judges can we get a ruling.

Yes! Judges say it's clearing a sort of "stance" any way you look at it but...

Nooooo. He can't hold it. He drops to seated at the edge of the bed. Exhausted. Farts.

Dread comes over him. It's time for SOCKS! He hates putting on socks. Plus he knows that to tug on a sock is no different than a pull on the finger. Bendamustine!

But wait. There's no reason for socks now.

Why?

Cuz it's

Summatime Summatime Sum Sum

Summatime

Summatime Summatime

Saaaaa ugh ma time . Yay!

Comments:

Bruce I love the way you describe things. Your humour is fantastic and always gives me a giggle. Thanks for brightening my day when I'm down 💋😂

I totally love this, Are you published? I would so read your book.

I love your humor

You have a great attitude, you will do well.

I love your humor!!! Blow that stuff out!!! Keep on getting better! I know I can get a laugh from your post and it makes my day!!!

I remember trying to learn how to do it back in HS, but never fully mastered it.

Bruce sounds like you need to put a holster on your belt for a bottle of free breeze to Cary everywhere with you. For that spring air smell Lol. Good luck with your treatment.

Blame it on the dog.... 😣

I absolutely love your humor and attitude! The way you type up your experience is amazing. Keep on strong

I'm sorry to laugh at your misery, but you just had to go and be so funny.

You have a gift😂. Thank you for lifting our day.

Best laugh of the day Bruce! Keep em coming.

I love you! 😂😂😂❤❤❤ Comedy is your way of coping and we get that and we are here for you!

ONG I haven't laughed this hard in years. This so funny, but I'm sorry you have to insure this awful pull my finger experience. Good luck Warrior 😱

It so hard going through all of this - we all know. Yet you can still find humor and make us laugh 😀. Thanks Bruce

You are amazing Bruce!❤

I'm sorry for your trials and tribulations but you do it with such good humor! They say, sometimes all you can do is laugh!

Your Fartadine must make you happy that you are currently single. You gave me quite a giggle. Hang in there Bruce. The good times are a comin.

Yup I gotta have humor to make it through to the other side of the journey while healing....😱

I love your attitude Bruce! 😀

Quanked!!

May 24, 2019 at 6:43 AM

Ok troops another day in MMville.

Recall that our hapless hero (ugh, me) was last on a journey of discovery regarding flatulence and the drug Bendamustine that is one half of his new therapy which he started up with on Monday.

The other half is four days in a row... 100mg each day... of Prednisone .

The "Mombo Combo".

Interestingly I segued from "exhausting" all throughout the house to being utterly consumed and just plain "exhausted".

Bendamustine fa fa fatigue by golly and whoa!

Now I'm "too pooped to pop" and "too tired to toot."

On my six year MM journey I've had my waltz with Revlimed fatigue and my slow dance with Pomalyst but hey this Bendamustine fatigue, yeah buddy when I first woke up....

Quanked! (Google it)

"Gush with life? Ha! No gush... I was barely a drizzle.

I stood.

Trudged to the kitchen for my 100mg of Prednisone.

That should get me moving soon enough.

I decide to change my T-shirt. I get the shirt off but the trudge and wrestle with that dang child proof lid on the Pred... It's all too much and I'm unable to pull the fresh shirt over my head.

Shirtless now... (settle down ladies)... I go to plan B... button front shirt... teal blue cotton with wrinkles on top da wrinkles.

I'm careful to button it all the way up to get past the "that's STILL there?" tumor slightly bulging on my sternum. (I've named it "Lumpy"... Gee Wally!)

Fa fa fatigue.

(Here's a shopping tip, MM travelers. Buy the Bounty brand paper towels. They tear soooo much easier on the perf than the Aldi store brand. Today I gave a thumbs up to Bounty brand.)

On to the recliner. Fosbury Flop.

Hee hee I'm such that I'm unable to fold my arms across my chest ... so they hang at my sides.

I know I'm alive because I can move my tongue.

Soon the Pred pokes and prods a bit of life into me. My sister and caregiver texts... "Yeah, all is well" I text back.

Ah so thankful for this glorious gift of a day.

And so it goes and so it goes.

******

BIG shout out to all you veterans. Thank you for your service.

Comments:

We have to laugh or we could cry all the time. Thanks for sharing this update. Funny to think your caregiver texted... Was she too scared of the side effect just to show up??? I know, leave the humor to you. Best wishes on your journey!

Living with Myeloma: not for wusses! Good on ya, Bruce.

What a surprise. I looked up "quanked" and there it was. A new word in my vocabulary and I can actually use it. Merci

Chin up ole boy, if you can lift it

Praise God for Steroids!!!💪 Shirtless selfie please! Hehe.....

Googled it! Quanked is a condition in which one's energy and vitality has been consumed. One who is quanked has used up his or her bodily or mental resources, usually because of arduous or long-sustained effort. To feel quanked at the end of the day; quanked after a hard run; feeling rather quanked; quanked by a long vigil.

Hang in there. Your humor is wonderful!

I am sorry you are having such a difficult time. Hang in there my friend.

Bad Limericks

May 30, 2019 at 1:37 PM

Some really bad limericks:

There is a mass on my chest that is tumorous
In my own special way I find that quite humorous
I doesn't go away
In the front it do stay
Now im all the more handsome and glamorous
**

Friends brought in food including quiche
So much... too much... Sheesh!
Eat it up or seem rude
It's just too much food
Pie... yep that's pie... I sure hope it's peach
**

In bed I roll into a wad... I'm coiled

There's no other like me, search the world

Then I'll stand up til I tump

And it's such that I'll claim to have toiled

**

"Change meds!!!" Doc put a call in
Now looks like my blood counts have fallen
And the cancer pulled back
From this recent attack
And that's great to know regardless the stage
ya'll in

****

Ok, folks you can do better than those... come on... add your own!!!

Comments:

I am glad that your numbers are better. I pray they continue getting better . May God bless you.

The pen be yours, sir. You'll not take a fancy to my limericks. Tho I did once write The Ruby Yacht by Oh Mae I Can.😮

Between two and twenty she said...

It's been three... I'm not dead.

Body stay in the show you've got seventeen to go

No.. I ain't taking THAT med

Great creative writing

I have a new pain in the neck!
I thought to myself what the heck!
I went to the doc, and she said with a bound
"looks like it's time for an ultrasound!"
I went today, 3 days to wait for the doc to read my fate! ❤

Love these. Thanks for keeping us smiling.

There once was a man from Nantucket... 😅 I'll stick to haikus.

Cancer Bows to a Smile

I went to my doctor today

He said my cancers at bay

I wish I could say,

the pain's gone away

But my bones scream at me

every day 😫

The Walker

June 3, 2019 at 11:35 AM

Days of Our Lives in MMville -

Now I can only walk using a "walker"...It's so bad I can't lift my legs to step onto the bathroom scale... I'm only attempting absolutely necessary tasks. Lucky for me getting my weight can wait. (Get it? I made that up!)

Whoa! What's happened to Bruce?

Well right now we don't have a dx but here's the back story: Two weeks ago I was infused with chemo drug Bendamustine and four days of really high dose prednisone followed. One week ago I was tired but, using a cane, was able to walk from the parking garage into the docs office. I even took a short stroll around the neighborhood with my new friend Kane.

On Friday though a weakness was set upon my arms and legs such that I had to end my new relationship with Kane. "It's not you, it's me." I tried to explain but Kane got all pissy and vowed never to speak to me again, Alas.

Rising from horizontal is only attempted when there's no other choice.

Time to call my caregiver sister to come stay with me. I promise to watch all her TV shows including the ones on HGTV where gay couples pick out a new home. (Actually , those shows are kinda cool.)

She gets me fed. Cleans up. Throws the Frizbee with dog Ellie. And switches me to a walker with PURPLE tennis balls on two leg tips. Oh boy!

I can get around now.

I send her home.

(Here's a tip. If you ever think you might need toilet handles install them long BEFORE you actually need them. I know this guy. And this guy waited until he could barely lean over to take on that task and this guy I know had a REALLY tough time at it.)

It's morning in MMville now.

So I make it to the toilet ... (I have new handles installed to help launch me off. Wheeee!)

And I walker down to the kitchen... feed the dog and make my coffee and toast.

My aim is to get to the recliner ... have my coffee and toast and call my MM team.

However... Ellie dog demands Frisbee time and my only choice is to comply. I horse the walker through the too narrow patio door... I'm outside barefoot and give the Frisbee a few feeble flips (Wow, Bruce can still do a bit of alliteration!.)

A MONSTER mosquito stabs my bare foot for his breakfast. That sends me back inside.

So how can I move me, the walker, a cup of coffee and my toast to the cell phone at the recliner? Walkers go up and down and any fool knows the coffee will spill.

Ain't no thang.

First I wipe up the coffee spilled from the first go at it. This time coffee goes into a cup with a screw on lid. That goes into my right jammie pants pocket. Toast goes into my left jammie pants pocket. (Note to self: DRY toast is probably a better way to go for now.)

Walker into the living room that I've recently renamed the "barely living room"... Fosbury Flop into the recliner.

The itch on my ankle from that mosquito is incredible and juuuust out of my now limited reach to scratch. I'll try to make up with Kane to get at that later.

I call the MM team. They are ON IT and I know I'll be fine. Perhaps this is caused by that high dose of pred... or the chemo drug they guess, and book me for labs and an appointment tomorrow.

"Nothing you can do for now. "

Sheesh they ain't kiddin.

Comments:

Every god i can think to pray to, every compassionate meditation i know, and every piece of my heart is focused on you getting better. And i pray too your sister stays with you until you overcome this. I appreciate your humor and positive attitude but please don't let it keep you from getting the help you so clearly need.

Way to make it through Bruce!! I'm glad you still have your humour. My fingers crossed

Gotta take hold of the situation and punch back.... and you did! They can take our mobility away, but they can't take our sense of humor.

Bruce, I have to admire your humor in all of this. I guess it's the way you cope with MM. I understand. Just hoping that you are not hurting too much or having too much of a problem walking. Please take care of yourself.

You are funny and that's good

Laughter & humor is good medicine.

Love you Bruce! You gave me such a smile today. . . And I needed it. Laughing may be our best medicine—you have an incredible way with words. Thank you again!

You are being a good sport about this! I can relate as I have been unable to walk hardly 10 to 20 steps for the past week. Lower back issues and severe nerve pain. Thank goodness for Kane.

"Nothing you can do for now" 😂😂

I use my rolling walker all the time. Its safety for me because I do not want to fall. In the house I don't use it, only when I wake up... that is my worst pain in the morning.

Funny yet poignant. Wishing you the best as you continue the fight.

You are so funny! Brighten my day. Good luck tomorrow. Note to self: Keep purple tennis balls and toilet rails on hand ...BEFORE needed!!! And jammies with deep pockets! Hang in there my Bud...Lots of luv & Hugs!

You're hillarious!!! Thank you for helping me start the day! 😂😂😂

Love the "barely living room"! Thanks for the entertainment, great fodder for your humor mill but I do hope your team gets it cleared up for you so you can get out and play with the dog in your shoes and socks!

Love the humor.....keeps us going. I live on sarcasm

I want to laugh and cry so I can't figure out which one to do!! Hope things get much better. Love your humor.

I have seen bags tied or hooked on the sides of walkers. Like a bike basket. Love your story

I loved my walker with wheels & hand brake! It had a seat built in too.

Lol, life throws us curves but u need to get an apron with pockets for the walker where u can stash breakfast for your journey to the yard and at least have u coffee while it's hot and put the toster in a ziplock bag but don't close it, or do like I do drink yogurt and have breakfast cookies but still get crumbs in the bed damit this cancer sucks

And as the ultimate compliment, I shall be stealing "barely-living room" when I need it!! :)

Bruce, your humor is a gift to all of us! As hard as things are, you make me laugh....then pray! I am praying for you, and for your sister (good woman)! Thank you for being you!

Carpenter's aprons work great on walkers! Sippy cups work well for transporting wine.😜

Back In The Hospital

June 5, 2019

Well we are moving along in this journey. I'm still not walkin but now I'm not walkin IN a hospital where a "Fall Risk" wrist band really means something.

"Mr. Morgan, walk on in". I'm welcomed... "Weren't you just in here?"

I say "It's Morton, not Morgan... yes I was here in March. This time I'm liveried in a wheel chair so 'Come on in' better says it."

We smile.

The doc wants more tests and it's early in the month so the hospital wants more butts in da beds.

I'm physically lifted onto the scale for weigh in. (Here's a tip: Ladies: if you've ever the urge to be rustled around and given a good squeeze. Arrive at the hospital pushed by a petite push person and demand to be weighed.)

I'm put in a "private" room with a pixilated/infrared camera shining down on my bed.

I'm read my restrictions. "NO WALKING AROUND, BUSTER". "If you need to use the lavatory, CALL A NURSE!!"

I almost pee my pants. Just a little. (I google the word "lavatory" later. Why not just SAY "bathroom" or even "the can?" Lavatory... sheesh.)

(Ok I'm just kidding about the team calling me "buster". My nurses and docs here are FABULOUS and would never talk to any patient like that.

I'm NOT kidding about my "almost a wee"... Hey! I hadda go, really.")

I'm pulled from the MRI tube at 10:30 pm. Yep that late… I'm an "urgent" gent. I am. I am.

"Why don't they come up with a quieter MRI machine??"

I asked the tech and he answered swiftly: "What? What? I didn't hear what you said".

Figures.

They scan my L3 and S2. That's the area recently buzzed with x-ray treatments. Perhaps they did not get all the tumors... Doh! or they left behind a scar behind my behind. Double Doh!

Right now (16 hours later) we are waiting for a radiologist to complete his "read" of the "urgent" MRI. The "read" is then made available juuuuust after the "you can't be released today, Mr. Morgan." time. Hmmmm. Funny how that happens.

So now we wait for the doc to read the report on the MRI. I order dinner. I'm stayin the night fur sure.

Comments:

Best of luck and get some rest. Praying for good results.

You crack me up

Admit it, you went back to get that wonderful hospital food. ☺

Keep fighting the good fight

You just can't seem to stay out of trouble! Thankfully, they haven't found your funny spot. . .

Yes, I hope the tumors stay away from your funny bone!

The hospital I go to has the best salmon. Everyone I know agrees. Find the best meal, order and sit back and enjoy.

Have a pleasant night Bruce

Bruce, I am wondering if you were the little boy who always got in trouble but really didn't mean to. I pray that the MRI read is good news. Enjoy your overnight vacation. Let us know how things are going.

🙏🙏🙏🙏🙏

🙏🙏🙏🙏🙏

Enjoy ☺ your vacation Bruce! Where else could you get waited on 24 hours a day!! Hope they can fix you up too.

Good thing you weren't really urgent!! I guess the silver lining is you have a team waiting on you hand and foot tonight. Enjoy it like a mini vacation. Is your sister watching your dog... Ellie is it? Hope you enjoy dinner! Another bright side you don't have to do the dishes. Sending hugs!

Sending gentle hugs

I think I'm praying the MRI is negative...i think that means showed up, like a cancerous tumor. Whichever, i hope the results are good news

What's an LP?

June 7, 2019 at 12:55 AM

So the doc said to me late yesterday "I want to give you an LP."

Great! I love record albums. My fav as a kid that I played 'til it wore out was "Why Is There Air?" by Bill Cosby. (What ever happened to the Cos, anyway?)

Well it turns out "LP" in doc speak is not a long playing record album.

In doc speak "LP" is "Lumbar Puncture"... formerly, lovingly called a "Spinal Tap" procedure. Gulp. Double gulp.

This gent's urgent MRI results showed nothing that might explain the weakness in his legs.

So we needed to rule out that myeloma bad guy cells had not entered into my spinal fluid. The way to do that is to go and look at sum dat fluid.

I said "Doc, how will I know what to look for?" And somewhat confused by my question he explained that THEY will inspect the fluid not me. Whew!

Ok what follows, for those who are curious, will inform what's involved in the LP procedure.

I'll start out and say there was absolutely NO PAIN involved. Nadda, zilch... nuttin! A VERY itty bitty needle goes in (not felt at all) after the local and VERY proper anesthesia has fully numbed the area in the small of the back. The 14ml amount needed is allowed to run softly into a vial. It's clear and somewhat thicker than water. Needle removal was not felt at all. After that I'm stuck on BandAid brand cuz BandAid stuck on me.

So. Piece of cake, right?

Not really.

A lumbar puncture or spinal tap by name just makes one pucker the pooper. That's why my doc just referred to it as an LP.

Yeah, yeah but in the hospital it was always called a lumbar puncture or (pucker tight) a lumbar "punch". Yikes!

And I suppose for liability reasons the patient "punchee" must be fully informed of ALL the risks of this VERY safe and VERY painless necessary and important diagnostic procedure.

So I was told much more than I needed to hear. They even had my voice recorded answering in the affirmative my understanding of all the "risks". All that hooey can cause to raise the patient's anxiety level up up and away.

I was determined to not have that happen so the "court jester" "class clown" element in my persona got dialed up and that helped to calm me . So myself, the administering doc and the techs enjoyed ourselves all while soaking in some Stevie Ray Vaughn on the tunes box .

Late in the day ... da da dummmmmm,... I get the "preliminary" report and no myeloma bad guys were found (Yay!) so the rest of my drain off was sent for a higher level look ..

"That report will take days to get back, so Mr. Morgan so you can go home to dog Ellie."

And the 40mg of Dex I'm getting daily is working to help my hobble. No pain at all anywhere either.

I'm at home in my comfy "barely living" living room.

And so it goes. And so it goes.

Comments:

Will continue to believe that the following reports will be just as wonderful for you.

Had an LP last November. No MM cells in fluid. But unlike you I screamed liked a frightened schoolgirl when that needle entered my spine!

Wow, I'd be scared to death. 40 Dex ain't no picnic either. I'm getting, if primary ever gets around to it, high dose amitriptyline so if pain isn't gone at least I'll be happy. Waiting for your next installment and hope it's good news.

You my friend, are priceless

I love your posts, make me smile xxx

YAY !! So far so good!! ☺

Keep on ... keeping on! 👋❤

I received a few bone marrow biopsy's where they go in my hip back bones for fluids and marrow. I received local when I was conceiving. Piece of cake 🍰 *kidding ;)*

Gordon Lightfoot

June 16, 2019 at 12:13 AM

Out of the hospital and back home just me and dog Ellie.

Update on me will close this post.

This here tonight is just a late night shout out asking you to share a story or two about a live concert (or series of concerts) you've attended.

I just went to see Gordon Lightfoot and another in our number just saw Foreigner live in concert.

Me going to see Lightfoot holds meaning because it was my fifth time to see him perform over a span of 47 years!

The first Lightfoot Concert I was 20 in 1972. This time it was on the eve of my 67 birthday and to make it inside I needed my walker with the cute purple tennis balls on the feet. (On the walker feet, not my feet...)

I could not have felt more blessed than to have made it into that hall for a live performance

I'll just now encourage each and every one of us to make it a point to see a live performance. Pick out a favorite entertainer ... get the best ticket you can afford and treat your caregiver to a night out.

Here's a tip. Call ahead to the theatre and tell them your cancer story and ask for special assistance. Oh my golly they will treat you oh so fine.

And we deserve some special attention, eh.

Do it. Go online and click click some tickets for you and your caregiver.

Ok. Now your turn.

Your very most memorable live concert. Tell us the story.

****

Update on Bruce -

My walking is improved though I'm grateful for my walker and my new best friend Kane.

I'll start physical therapy on Thursday and hopefully Irish folk dancing soon thereafter .

The secret sauce of Bendamustine infusion and mega doses of prednisone will resume on Monday because the 4 week blood draw showed a dramatic drop in my LLC. Yay! The stuff works!!!

Thanks to you all for prayers and sending smiles my way.

Comments:

I went to many great concerts over the years. The one that has stayed with me the most was when The Who debuted the rock opera Tommy at the Electric Factory in Philadelphia. Songs from that play in my head to this day. I also saw it as a performance with others singing and acting out the roles in Montreal and NYC

I have seen Elton John 4 times.. 3 times at Dodger Stadium. Can't manage that anymore. Good for you!!

Elvis! 1957 in San Francisco. Yup, I'm old. My best friend had won a contest. She had an interview with Elvis! He signed his album, "Loving you allways"! 😊

Love Jimmy Buffett. Try to go every other year! Last year had to bring my oxygen 😂

The Boss - Bruce Springsteen

Elton John and Billy Joel (Tickets were a Christmas gift). It was the first time I had been to that venue. A gentleman a few rows below us commented, "You have to be a goat to get to these seats." True enough. The lady behind me asked if I even knew the words to any of the songs. I did not look like "the type." Yeah all of them. She kept yelling Benny and the Jets any time Elton sang. It was a very long concert. Toward the end I had to make use of the facilities. They sang her song. My sister commented," That lady is happy now.

Or in my case, most recently, musical theatre... on an unexpectedly free night at short notice, l treated myself to a ticket to…

My significant other and I have spent our summers especially attending live concerts over the years. Our range of music genres is all over the map Steve Miller, Billy Joel, Farm Aid Concert, Bluegrass Festivals, etc. I love Norah Jones voice so he is taking me next week. I got diagnosed last Fall I am close to 100 days sct and will prob need a walker. I have been worried so you just have made me feel better and excited now.

We have tickets to see Earth, Wind & Fire in a couple weeks. Jimmy Buffett this July! And Morris Day and the Time twice this year...

I've seen Dan Fogelberg in concert 4 times before his death due to cancer. My fave by far was when he had a gig in Chicago, but made a special appearance in South Bend, IN (just south of our home in MI) for "An Acoustic Evening With Dan". It was lovely, and not as ear splitting as concerts usually are. 🎼

We saw the Eagles in Chicago and it was great. Loaded up on Imodium and rocking out.

So glad to read your post....I always get a chuckle from them! Keep 'em coming!!

Was fortunate to run a small Artist Series as part of the Regional Campuses of Miami University for 33 years. Some of the Artists presented were Randy Newman, Keb' Mo, Bela Fleck and the Flecktones, Diana Krall, Alison Krauss and many more.

The last concert I went to was this past October—Jason Isbel at the John Paul Jones arena in Charlottesville, Va. I had been feeling really anxious about an upcoming bone marrow biopsy, and my dear husband planned a night out to be a distraction

I went to many great concerts over the years. The one that has stayed with me the most was when The Who debuted the rock opera Tommy at the Electric Factory in Philadelphia. Songs from that play in my head to this day. I also saw it as a performance with others singing and acting out the roles in Montreal and NYC.

Feel the Burn?

June 18, 2019 at 3:33 AM

"If it starts to burn in your arm, you tell us, ok?"

Lemme tell ya folks, hearing that from the infusion nurse is no way to begin the day.

So here's the skinny... at least my version anyway.

This Bendamustine drug I'm getting infused into me is the real deal a genuine chemo drug and the stuff is rather caustic and can irritate at the point of infusion such that there's the possibility of a pretty good "oh my!" from the get go. Feel the Burn, yeah.

My role is to lay there toes up in anticipation. And wait.

Drip. Drip. Drip.

While I wait, this Cancer Center, in addition to support dogs to pet, has a volunteer amateur magician who did knot tricks and "where's the pea under the walnut shell" to get my mind off my assignment to "tell us if it starts to burn."

Well, no, it didn't burn at all. And, guess what… a sap like me with chemo brain finds no pleasure in that stupid pea under the walnut shell game.

And tomorrow is dose two day.

Drip. Drip. Drip.

I'm hopeful it's "belly dancer day" but I figure that's regarded as inappropriate.

Tonight I won't sleep a wink cuz I'm dosed up on Prednisone. My mind still stuck on that pea under which walnut shell challenge.

And so it goes. And so it goes.

Comments:

Maybe if you had guessed the correct shell, the prize would have been a belly dancer for entertainment tomorrow.

You made me smile ❤

Love your humor, Bruce! You make me laugh outloud! And you help me try to stay in each moment, one day a time.

When I was hospitalized a couple years ago, the staff said there was a harpist who went from room to room playing. Maybe she can come to accompany the belly dancer.

Love you Bruce—keep up the commentary—and keep up your wonderful spirit! You lift us all.

Thanks for the encouragement that means a lot to me.

Good luck tomorrow. Pet the dogs 🐕

I'm pulling for you, Bruce. Hope there IS a belly dancer, even if it's just in your head!❤

Bring your own belly dancer!

Are you really at the cancer center or at home in la la land. Never heard of entertainment. Good Luck!

Good luck.

Your post made me laugh

Support dogs and candy? I'm jealous.

Maybe if you had guessed the correct shell, the prize would have been a belly dancer for entertainment tomorrow.

Love your humor, Bruce! You make me laugh outloud! And you help me try to stay in each moment, one day a time.

Call Out to Bruce From the Group

June 28, 2019

Hey Mr. Bruce Morton! Haven't heard from you in a few days. How are you feeling? Life is just not the same without some Bruce humor. Hope all is well.

(BGM) Yes you are right. Expect a post from me tonight. All is well but my constant travel companion (the MM) has been nagging for some attention. I trust all is well with you—I've been keeping up with everyone best I could. Thank you for thinking of me.

Comments:

I love how you describe your MM... constant travel companion. Lightens it somehow. Hope today is a better day for you!

... glad you asked. I thought this too last night, at midnight. Then, with the morning light the thought was gone.

hang in there....all of us want to continue to read your humor. Your humor is a help to the rest of us MM friends.

Me, too.

Definitely!

I'm a new member and am anxious to see/read your humor and thoughts.

Days Like These

June 28, 2019 at 7:24 PM

"Nobody told me there'd be days like these." Sing it John Lennon. Strange days indeed.

Now I can usually wring a yuck yuck out of most any situation (though I've finally learned to lay off the whistling at funerals.)

But lately my MM has been feedin me nuttin to yank a good har har from.

I'd been training myself 'cause sure as shootin I knew the days would come when this incurable cancer just wasn't funny...even to me.

And for a while... just a while... the MM had the upper hand on me. The big blow came a few weeks ago when... suddenly... I lost my ability to walk. Yep. Suddenly. One day I was a walking and the next day I weren't. Huh? What's up with that?

That startled even my doc who immediately put me in the hospital for tests which ended up proving not much. That was back on June 4 and since then I've managed to go from needing a walker to just needing a cane much of the time. It's being called steroid myopathy.

Nothing funny in that I'm afraid.

Nope.

Until, finally this week I scored a "reverse control" wrestling move on my cancer. Yay! Finally. (That's like a collegiate wrestling move none of that WWF stuff.)

Here's the set up. My sister and caregiver, Karen, is the WORST EVER at guiding a wheelchair. Going through any door way she will hit BOTH door jambs. Hit the right jamb which means we then slam into the left jamb. It's not unusual for her to lodge the wheelchair fully stuck between the two jambs. So we leave the doc's office on Tuesday. I walked in using my best friend Kane but that left me too tired to walk out. I was through for the day. Now my only choice was to gird my loins and ride in a big monster size hospital wheel chair with Karen doing the pushing.

Headed to the outer waiting room now and Karen did not disappoint. That made everyone in the waiting room look up from reading "Cancer Tips" magazine.

So she and I started to laughing which really gets everyone's attention.

Next I take Kane and pretend it's not a cane but rather a canoe paddle and Karen and I paddle that wheelchair right through the crowd. That got everyone to laughing... really quite loudly.

So there we all were, "sick" with our cancers laughing like little school kids.

Fun.

The rest of the way to the car I alternated from the boat paddle routine to a Queen Elizabeth twist-the-wrist wave.

More fun. Hee hee and ya huck!

That was just silly fun. (Silly fun with the BESTEST CAREGIVER EVER...Thanks for putting up with me, sister Karen!)

And so it goes and so it goes.

Comments:

Bruce, only you can make this horrid disease funny! Never ever stop entertaining us!!!

You are amazing!

Sitting in my "Barely Living Room" enjoying your humor at 1:30 am! Thanks so much for sharing your wonderful humor with all of us!

Bruce, I need to ask you. What is steroid mypopathy? I sincerely hope that they can find a solution to that and you can walk again.

(BGM) long term use of steroids can weaken muscles. The muscles in my upper left leg went to heck a few weeks ago. I've started physical therapy and we are hopeful that I can get the strength that lost back. I'd like to be able wave off steroids in the future but I doubt I'll get away with that.

"Cancer Tips" ?!?! BWAHAHAHAHAHA!!!!! That is hysterical! I ALWAYS enjoy reading your posts. So sorry about your walking struggles but I'm glad you still have your sense of humor!I hope they find a solution for you soon! Keep your chin up!!

You helped me today.

Bruce Morton, You are Blessed to have a wonderful sister like Karen. Is she as funny as you?

Oh how you make me laugh Bruce!! What a great personality you have... With everything that's happening with your MM and you still manage to give us uplifting posts. You are lucky to have your sister as your carer, she sounds amazing too. Keep up the good fight, I am praying for you!! Love to you and your sister xx

Where is the book!! "The Life of an MM Fighter!" And that's not like an MMA fighter. 😂. Bruce my friend, you never disappoint! Keep 'em coming. 😀.

You seem to find some humor in any situation. I love your posts. They always give me a smile.

While surely tiresome these posts can be lately, you bring life to the rest of us!! I am so sorry for the hard times you are going through. Remember, one day at a time, my friend. Thinking of you.

Bruce Morton, you are amazing! Prayers that you'll regain your mobility. Your sister sounds like a pretty special person even if she isn't the greatest wheelchair driver. ☺

Better to laugh than cry. You gave every person in that waiting room a precious gift.

Bruce, I try to find humor in all my MM issues, but you, my friend, definitely have me beat! While I'm so very sorry at all the discomfort you go through I absolutely love the way you write about your trials and tribulations. Know you are bringing smiles and chuckles to those who need it. Sorry it is at your expense, but know we love you for it!

I love the positive attitude. You should consider writing a "cancer in comedy" whitepaper or book perhaps entitled, "The funny things about MM".....godspeed on your recovery!!

Keep the day bright for those around you and your day will be brightened in return.

Once again, you are a pure demonstration of in spirit of being alive! Thank you Bruce!

Nothing better than reading one of your posts right smack in the middle of a crappy day... thanks for the laugh Bruce...I sure needed it!

Hugs and kisses that they come up with an answer to your lack of mobility. Sounds like you have a wonderful, fun family. God bless, glad you had the strength to update us. We miss you. Even if you just tell us all to F off, because that's all you can get out that day, as long as we hear from you.

OMG. Thank you so much for the laugh and the image of you paddling the wheelchair. Wonderful sense of humor that I needed just now.
Hide or report this

I'm new here and just getting to know your beautiful spirit. Thanks for sharing your journey and your lite hardheartedness. You are a jewel, my friend. Sending prayer and good vibes.

Wonderful! Reminds me of something I read...

"This moment is not life waiting to happen, goals waiting to be achieved, words waiting to be spoken, connections waiting to be made, regrets waiting to evaporate, aliveness waiting to be felt, enlightenment waiting to be gained.
No. Nothing is waiting.
This is it. This moment is life."

You have a hilarious sense of humor, I will try to grab a bit more sleep with those images of you padding the wheelchair and doing her majesty's wave ! Lol !

I needed that laugh this morning...Thank you for such a beautiful spirit & sharing with us ☺

A GOOD ATTITUDE

hope you continue to improve with your walking. And again, just love reading your posts. I agree...you should write a book!!

I've been thinking about you lately Bruce, and hoping all was well, but this little voice in the back of my mind kept saying you were having a hard time. You can put a bright outlook on the worst of circumstances, and it's good to hear from you again. I'm hoping you continue to get stronger. ❤

Love your spirit and attitude. thank you!

Bruce you are just too funny. I read all your posts but have never commented I have only enjoyed. You have such a wonderful sense of humour .. thank you for making me giggle and, always, leaving your followers with smiles on our faces. I wish you the best of everything on your journey.

Keep up the good humor not meaning the ice cream man but your own humor. You cold be a stand comic Especially once you can stand without assistance. Hope you're feeling better soon. Do many surprises with this cancer good and bad. Take care my MM friend

Love that getting the whole center involved in the laugh!! Goos for you Bruce Morton, hope you keep laughing your way stronger!

Thank you for an awesome post!

LOL

I am sorry for your rough times. I love the canoe paddle bit. Most of all, I was so blessed by the laughter you spread at the hospital and in our group. Keep your chin up and laughter in your heart. You are one amazing man.

Not sure I could be as upbeat as you in your shoes. But glad you can see some levity in the moment and keep on going!! Hang in there.

☹ *and as usual* 😃

Humor is the best medicine now isn't it? Praying for you Bruce and hoping clarity comes ori answers show up as to why you can't walk.

And So It Goes, And So It Goes

June 30, 2019

Well, we have come to a good "stopping place" for this Volume 1 of my postings and the comments from the members of the MM FB groups.

And to repeat, I've included all those "great humor, Bruce, keep it up" comments just to remind myself and all of us how important it is to smile all throughout our MM journey. My goal in posting about my journey is to generate smiles and laughter out there in MMville. I'm convinced that smiles and laughter throughout our travels with MM gives power and strength to us as we push back at this disease. When you are up against a tough day, remember: Cancer Bows to a Smile

Bruce Morton
June 30, 2019

Glossary and Abbreviations

MM:	Multiple Myeloma
BMB:	Bone Marrow Biopsy
LP:	Lumbar Puncture test
SCT:	Stem Cell Transplant procedure
CAR-T:	A new and promising treatment for MM... Google it
DEX:	Dexamethasone steroid given as an injection or orally
EDS	Emergency Defecation Situation
IWEDS	In Walmart Emergency Defecation Situation
LLC	Lambda Light Chain
Darza	Darzalex
Pred	Prednisone Steroid
THS	The Hershey Squirts

Please Donate to St. Jude Children's Research Hospital

For many years, my charity of choice has been St. Jude Children's Research Hospital.

St. Jude's is doing fabulous work… saving kids' lives. They are wonderful stewards of the money that is donated to them. Please go to stjude.org and give $20 or more if you can. Hey, no kid should have to struggle with cancer, and no young family should be burdened having to pay for cancer care.

Thanks.

Made in the USA
Middletown, DE
13 August 2023